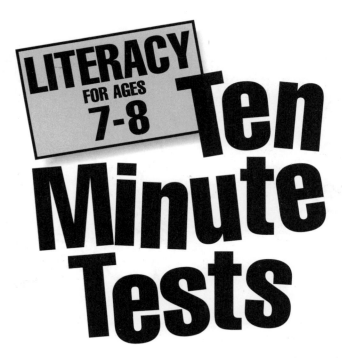

LITERACY
FOR AGES 7-8
Ten Minute Tests

CONTENTS

Louis Fidge

A **prefix** is a group of letters we put **in front** of a word.
Prefixes **change the meaning** of the word.

well

unwell

Colour in your score on the testometer!

Choose the prefix un **or** dis **to complete each word.**

1. _____pack

2. _____well

3. _____place

4. _____trust

5. _____fair

6. _____happy

7. _____agree

8. _____may

9. _____load

10. _____bolt

11. _____honest

12. _____do

13. _____arm

14. _____charge

15. _____cover

15
14
13
12
11
10
9
8
7
6
5
4
3
2
1

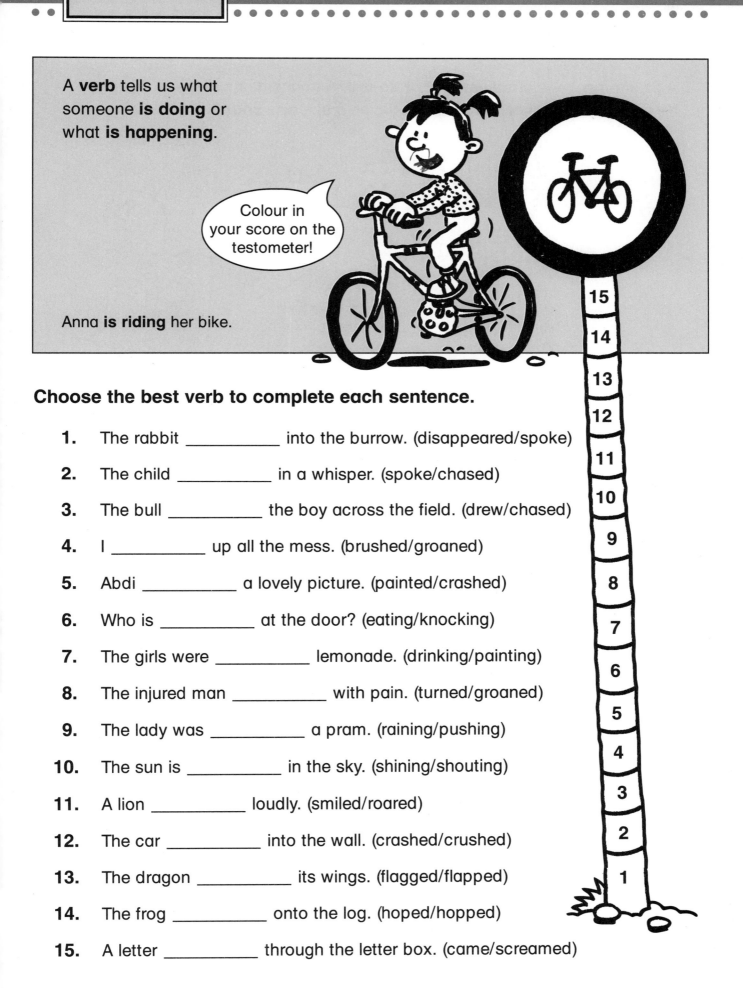

A **verb** tells us what someone **is doing** or what **is happening**.

Colour in your score on the testometer!

Anna **is riding** her bike.

Choose the best verb to complete each sentence.

1. The rabbit _____ into the burrow. (disappeared/spoke)

2. The child _____ in a whisper. (spoke/chased)

3. The bull _____ the boy across the field. (drew/chased)

4. I _____ up all the mess. (brushed/groaned)

5. Abdi _____ a lovely picture. (painted/crashed)

6. Who is _____ at the door? (eating/knocking)

7. The girls were _____ lemonade. (drinking/painting)

8. The injured man _____ with pain. (turned/groaned)

9. The lady was _____ a pram. (raining/pushing)

10. The sun is _____ in the sky. (shining/shouting)

11. A lion _____ loudly. (smiled/roared)

12. The car _____ into the wall. (crashed/crushed)

13. The dragon _____ its wings. (flagged/flapped)

14. The frog _____ onto the log. (hoped/hopped)

15. A letter _____ through the letter box. (came/screamed)

15
14
13
12
11
10
9
8
7
6
5
4
3
2
1

A **phoneme** is the **smallest unit of sound**. A phoneme may be made up of **one or more letters** which make **one sound**.

b + oa + t = boat

This word is made by using three phonemes.

Choose the correct phoneme to complete each word.

1.   m_____n (oo/ir)

2.   tr_____t (ee/ea)

3.   gr_____ (ow/oo)

4.   gl_____ (ue/oo)

5.   r_____d (oa/ow)

6.   cl_____ (aw/ow)

7.   p_____nt (au/ai)

8.   b_____n (ir/ur)

9.   _____l (ay/ow)

10. th_____sty (oo/ir)

11. yesterd_____ (ai/ay)

12. narr_____ (ow/aw)

13. r_____nd (ow/ou)

14. s_____cer (ou/au)

15. b_____l (oi/oa)

There are lots of words that end in **le**.

Colour in your score on the testometer!

a sing**le** eag**le**

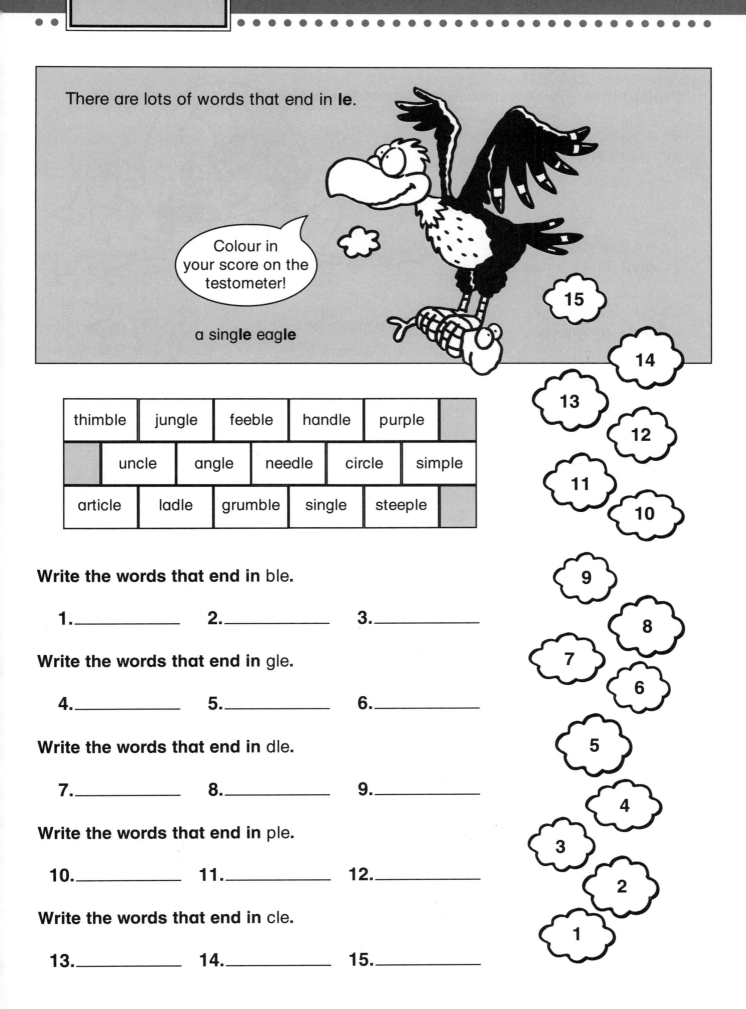

thimble	jungle	feeble	handle	purple	
uncle	angle	needle	circle	simple
article	ladle	grumble	single	steeple	

Write the words that end in ble.

1._____ 2._____ 3._____

Write the words that end in gle.

4._____ 5._____ 6._____

Write the words that end in dle.

7._____ 8._____ 9._____

Write the words that end in ple.

10._____ 11._____ 12._____

Write the words that end in cle.

13._____ 14._____ 15._____

Test 5 — Punctuation marks

Punctuation marks make writing **easier to read**.

Most sentences end with a **full stop**.

This is an alien.

If it is a **question**, a **question mark** is needed.

What is this?

We put an **exclamation mark** when we **feel strongly** about something.

What a strange alien!

Put in the missing punctuation mark in each sentence.

1. Where do you come from

2. What a funny name

3. The spaceship landed

4. A door opened slowly

5. Run for your life

6. Who is there

7. What do you want

8. It's not fair

9. This is terrible

10. The sun set in the sky

11. The bees buzzed near the flowers

12. How did the car crash

13. When did the letter come

14. Stop that at once

15. We have sausages and chips for tea

Colour in your score on the testometer!

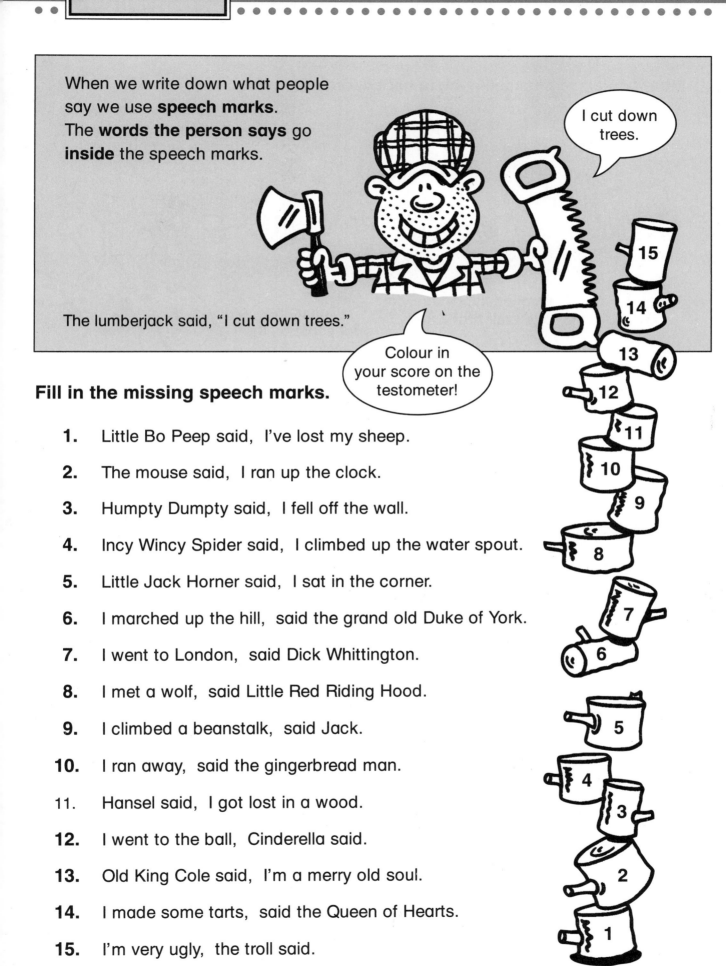

When we write down what people say we use **speech marks**. The **words the person says** go **inside** the speech marks.

I cut down trees.

The lumberjack said, "I cut down trees."

Colour in your score on the testometer!

Fill in the missing speech marks.

1. Little Bo Peep said, I've lost my sheep.

2. The mouse said, I ran up the clock.

3. Humpty Dumpty said, I fell off the wall.

4. Incy Wincy Spider said, I climbed up the water spout.

5. Little Jack Horner said, I sat in the corner.

6. I marched up the hill, said the grand old Duke of York.

7. I went to London, said Dick Whittington.

8. I met a wolf, said Little Red Riding Hood.

9. I climbed a beanstalk, said Jack.

10. I ran away, said the gingerbread man.

11. Hansel said, I got lost in a wood.

12. I went to the ball, Cinderella said.

13. Old King Cole said, I'm a merry old soul.

14. I made some tarts, said the Queen of Hearts.

15. I'm very ugly, the troll said.

Many books are arranged in **alphabetical order**.

These words are arranged in alphabetical order according to their **second** letter.

anteater   bear   camel   deer   dog   duck

These words are arranged in alphabetical order according to their **first** letter.

Colour in your score on the testometer!

Order these words according to their first letter.

1. bat dog cat _____

2. goat elephant fox _____

3. hen kangaroo jaguar _____

4. ostrich monkey lion _____

5. rat seal penguin _____

6. zebra swan panda _____

7. hamster mouse donkey beetle _____

8. ox worm donkey giraffe _____

Order these words according to their second letter.

9. crab cow cat _____

10. bird bull bear _____

11. parrot pike pelican _____

12. shark sardine snake _____

13. trout tiger turtle toad _____

14. giraffe gnu goat gerbil _____

15. bee badger bird buffalo _____

15
14
13
12
11
10
9
8
7
6
5
4
3
2
1

Yesterday I **rode** a horse.

I **am riding** my bike.

This is happening **now**, so the verb is in the **present tense**.

This happened in the **past**, so the verb is in the **past tense**.

Join up each verb with its past tense.

Colour in your score on the testometer!

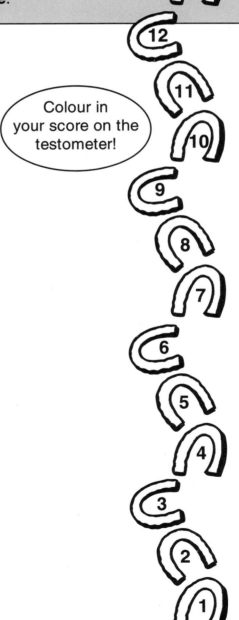

1.	walk	hopped
2.	hop	moved
3.	carry	copied
4.	move	walked
5.	arrive	held
6.	beg	carried
7.	copy	spoke
8.	hold	wrote
9.	bring	came
10.	see	taught
11.	speak	arrived
12.	take	brought
13.	teach	took
14.	write	begged
15.	come	saw

We use **commas** to **separate items in a list**.
We do **not** usually put a comma before the word **and**.

Colour in your score on the testometer!

Out of the window I saw a bus, a car, a van and a lorry.

Put in the missing commas in these sentences.

1. My friends are Sam Emma Abdi and Shanaz.

2. March June May and July are months of the year.

3. I like red blue yellow and green.

4. The four seasons are spring summer autumn and winter.

5. I have a dog a cat a fish and a budgie.

6. I hate sprouts cabbage parsnips and leeks.

7. I would like a bike a pen a book and a bag for Christmas.

8. Art science music and maths are good subjects.

9. In my bag I have a pen a ruler a rubber and a book.

10. London Rome Paris and Vienna are all capital cities.

11. I have been to France Spain Greece and Malta.

12. On the farm I saw some cows sheep pigs and hens.

13. On the rock there was a beetle an ant a slug and a snail.

14. Crisps chips chocolate and biscuits are not healthy.

15. In the sky you can see clouds the sun the moon and stars.

15
14
13
12
11
10
9
8
7
6
5
4
3
2
1

If you look closely, sometimes you can see **small words inside longer words**.

Colour in your score on the testometer!

There is an **ape** with a **cap** and a **cape** inside **escape**!

Find a small word 'hiding' in each of these words.

1. father _____

2. mother _____

3. heard _____

4. money _____

5. know _____

6. because _____

7. suddenly _____

8. friend _____

9. many _____

10. wheel _____

11. stage _____

12. question _____

13. narrow _____

14. rhyme _____

15. mystery _____

15
14
13
12
11
10
9
8
7
6
5
4
3
2
1

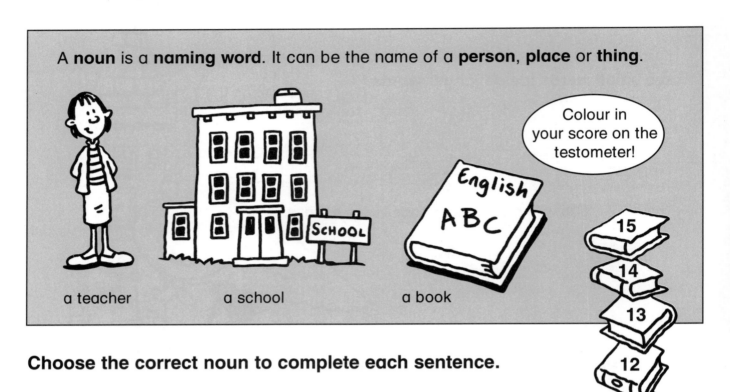

A **noun** is a **naming word**. It can be the name of a **person**, **place** or **thing**.

a teacher   a school   a book

Colour in your score on the testometer!

Choose the correct noun to complete each sentence.

1. A _____ makes things from wood. (mechanic/carpenter)

2. A _____ makes clothes. (tailor/grocer)

3. A _____ works on a farm. (baker/farmer)

4. A _____ rides horses in races. (diver/jockey)

5. An _____ looks after people's eyes. (doctor/optician)

6. Aeroplanes fly from an _____. (abbey/airport)

7. You can get petrol from a _____ . (garden/garage)

8. Ships load and unload at a _____. (dock/church)

9. We keep books in a _____. (lighthouse/library)

10. A _____ is where a king or queen lives. (palace/park)

11. We wash ourselves in a _____. (bed/sink)

12. A _____ is a baby's bed. (cot/cup)

13. Water is boiled in a _____.(knife/kettle)

14. We stir hot drinks with a _____. (spoon/stool)

15. Clothes are kept in a _____. (toaster/wardrobe)

A noun may be **singular** (when there is **only one** thing).
A noun may be **plural** when there is **more** than one thing).

one bus (singular)   two buses (plural)

Colour in your score on the testometer!

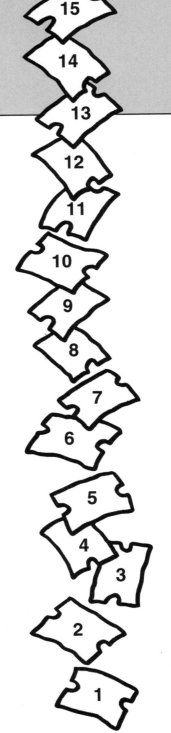

Complete these phrases.
Be careful with some of the spellings!

1. one chair, lots of _____

2. one fox, lots of _____

3. one coach, lots of _____

4. one bush, lots of _____

5. one glass, lots of _____

6. one berry, lots of _____

7. one child, lots of _____

8. one man, lots of _____

9. one _____, lots of bikes

10. one _____, lots of boxes

11. one _____, lots of bunches

12. one _____, lots of dishes

13. one _____, lots of copies

14. one _____, lots of lorries

15. one _____, lots of sheep

Some words contain **silent letters**. We cannot hear the letters when we say the words.

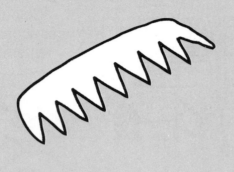

com**b**

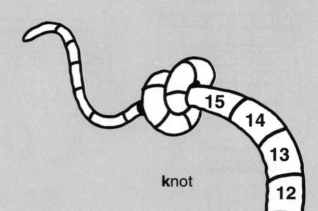

knot

Choose k or w to complete each word.

1. ____rite

2. ____nee

3. ____now

4. ____reck

5. ____rist

6. ____restle

7. ____nock

8. ____night

Choose b or g to complete each word.

9. num____

10. ____nat

11. clim____

12. crum____

13. thum____

14. ____nome

15. ____naw

Colour in your score on the testometer!

An **adjective** is a **describing** word. It tells us more about a **noun**.

Colour in your score on the testometer!

a **small** puppy

Choose the best adjective from the list below to go with each noun.

busy	handsome	dirty	old	beautiful
	straight	sharp	heavy	funny	tall
open	muddy	loud	empty	fizzy

1. a _____ weight
2. a _____ ruler

3. a _____ tree
4. a _____ clown

5. a _____ noise
6. a _____ puddle

7. a _____ mark
8. a _____ drink

9. an _____ door
10. a _____ road

11. an _____ glass
12. an _____ ruin

13. a _____ princess
14. a _____ knife

15. a _____ prince

A **suffix** is a **group of letters** we add to the **end** of a word.
A suffix changes the **meaning** of the word or the **job** the word does.

Colour in your score on the testometer!

power + ful
= powerful

power + less
= powerless

Add ful to the end of each word. Write the words you make.

1. colour _____

2. pain _____

3. care _____

4. thank _____

5. help _____

Add less to the end of each word. Write the words you make.

6. use _____

7. hope _____

8. thought _____

9. law _____

10. help _____

Take the suffix off each word. Write the words you are left with.

11. wonderful _____

12. heartless _____

13. graceful _____

14. faithless _____

15. pitiful _____

15
14
13
12
11
10
9
8
7
6
5
4
3
2
1

A **compound word** is a word made up of **two smaller words**.

Colour in your score on the testometer!

hand + bag = handbag

Do these word sums.

1. horse + shoe = _____

2. birth + day = _____

3. foot + step = _____

4. out + side = _____

5. with + out = _____

6. some + one = _____

7. grand + father = _____

8. hair + brush = _____

Write the two words that make up each of these compound words.

9. snowman _____ _____

10. motorway _____ _____

11. toothpaste _____ _____

12. cupboard _____ _____

13. eyesight _____ _____

14. wallpaper _____ _____

15. tablecloth _____ _____

The **subject** (the main person or thing) and the **verb** in each sentence must **agree**.

Colour in your score on the testometer!

The birds is flying. ☒   The birds are flying. ☑

Choose the correct form of the verb for each sentence.

1. Bells _____. (ring/rings)

2. The wind _____. (blow/blows)

3. A door _____. (open/opens)

4. Aeroplanes _____. (fly/flies)

5. An owl _____. (hoot/hoots)

6. Chickens _____ eggs. (lay/lays)

7. A rabbit _____ in a burrow. (live/lives)

8. Wolves _____. (howl/howls)

9. Mice _____. (squeak/squeaks)

10. I _____ my dinner. (eat/eats)

11. The children _____ to school. (go/goes)

12. Ben _____ a cold. (has/have)

13. The lady _____ some bread. (buy/buys)

14. Frogs _____. (hop/hops)

15. A cow _____ us milk. (give/gives)

15
14
13
12
11
10
9
8
7
6
5
4
3
2
1

A **collective noun** is the name given to a **group** of things.

a **herd** of cows

Colour in your score on the testometer!

| bunch | box | library | flock | swarm |
| chest | shoal | fleet |

Choose the best collective noun to complete each phrase.

1. a _____ of matches
2. a _____ of sheep
3. a _____ of bees
4. a _____ of drawers
5. a _____ of ships
6. a _____ of fish
7. a _____ of flowers
8. a _____ of books

| sticks | stones | singers | cornflakes |
| soldiers | trees | bananas |

Choose the best word to complete each phrase.

9. a choir of _____
10. an army of _____
11. a packet of _____
12. a forest of _____
13. a bunch of _____
14. a bundle of _____
15. a pile of _____

15
14
13
12
11
10
9
8
7
6
5
4
3
2
1

We can classify adjectives according to type. These adjectives describe size.

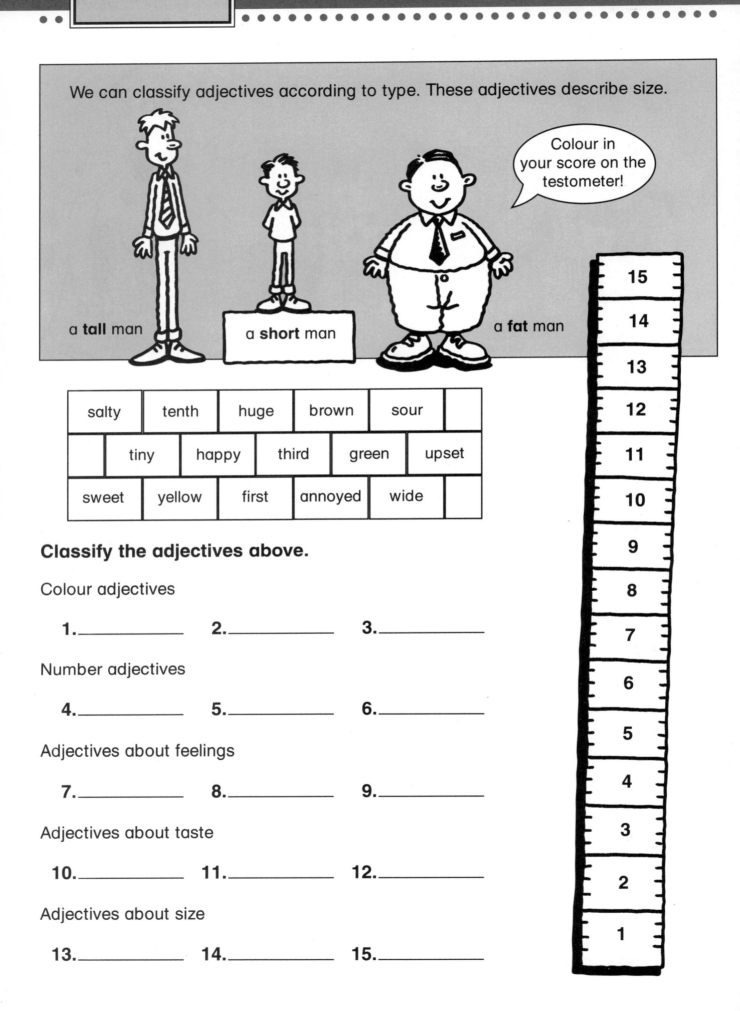

a **tall** man

a **short** man

a **fat** man

Colour in your score on the testometer!

salty	tenth	huge	brown	sour	
	tiny	happy	third	green	upset
sweet	yellow	first	annoyed	wide	

Classify the adjectives above.

Colour adjectives

1._____ 2._____ 3._____

Number adjectives

4._____ 5._____ 6._____

Adjectives about feelings

7._____ 8._____ 9._____

Adjectives about taste

10._____ 11._____ 12._____

Adjectives about size

13._____ 14._____ 15._____

15
14
13
12
11
10
9
8
7
6
5
4
3
2
1

When we say a word slowly, we can break it down into **smaller parts**. These parts are called **syllables**. Each syllable must contain at least **one vowel**.

Colour in your score on the testometer!

car
(one syllable)

lor + ry
(two syllables)

bull + do + zer
(three syllables)

Say these words slowly. Then write down if they have one, two or three syllables.

1. bus ☐

2. jet ☐

3. ambulance ☐

4. hovercraft ☐

5. ferry ☐

6. drum ☐

7. violin ☐

8. rocket ☐

9. trumpet ☐

10. caravan ☐

11. glider ☐

12. coach ☐

13. aeroplane ☐

14. tractor ☐

15. jeep ☐

A **prefix** is a **group of letters** we put in front of a word. Prefixes **change the meaning** of the word.

behave   **mis**behave

Colour in your score on the testometer!

Choose the prefix re or pre to begin each word.

1. _____turn

2. _____heat

3. _____fix

4. _____view

5. _____pay

6. _____mind

7. _____fill

8. _____fund

Choose the prefix mis or ex to begin each word.

9. _____judge

10. _____handle

11. _____port

12. _____spell

13. _____lead

14. _____plode

15. _____pand

A **pronoun** is a word that takes the place of a **noun**.

Colour in your score on the testometer!

Ben cried when Ben hurt his leg.   Ben cried when **he** hurt his leg.

Choose the best pronoun to complete each sentence.

1.   The lady went in the shop. _____ bought some apples. (He/She)

2.   _____ am always busy. (We/I)

3.   The boy shouted when _____ scored a goal. (he/they)

4.   "Why are _____ late?" Mr Shah asked Abdi. (you/he)

5.   "_____ are going to the park," the children said. (We/It)

6.   _____ is a lovely day. (It/You)

7.   Are _____ good at writing? (he/you)

8.   _____ like playing games. (We/It)

9.   The girl fell off her bike when _____ crashed. (she/you)

10. When the dog stopped _____ barked. (it/they)

11. The prince got up. _____ got dressed. (She/He)

12. I tried to lift the box but _____ was too heavy. (we/it)

13. When I shouted at the birds _____ flew away. (it/they)

14. The boy walked with the girl. _____ went in the park. (We/They)

15. When the man stopped _____ sat down. (you/he)

15
14
13
12
11
10
9
8
7
6
5
4
3
2
1

Antonyms are words that have the **opposite** meaning.

open   closed

Colour in your score on the testometer!

Join up the pairs of words with the opposite meaning.

1.	wild	white
2.	low	hot
3.	rough	tame
4.	black	bottom
5.	cheap	high
6.	cold	dear
7.	difficult	smooth
8.	wide	arrive
9.	top	empty
10.	first	easy
11.	near	left
12.	under	far
13.	depart	narrow
14.	right	over
15.	full	last

When we are writing about **ourselves** we write in the **first person**. We use pronouns like **I** and **we**.

When we are writing about **others** we write in the **third person**. We use pronouns like **he**, **she**, **it** and **they**.

I called for Ben.
We went swimming.

Annie and Lucy were surprised when **they** opened the box.

Colour in your score on the testometer!

Say if each of the pronouns marked in bold is in the first or third person.

1. **I** went to school. _____

2. Tom went out when **he** finished washing up. _____

3. The children chattered as **they** ate the bananas. _____

4. When the dog appeared **it** ran straight home. _____

5. The flowers looked lovely. **They** were all different colours. _____

6. **We** went to the cinema in the evening. _____

7. May **I** have some, please? _____

8. "**We** can do it!" Tom and Ben shouted. _____

9. The machine made a loud noise when **it** was turned on. _____

10. **I** am older than Sam. _____

11. Mr Shah went to bed. **He** went straight to sleep. _____

12. The lady was happy but **she** didn't smile. _____

13. **They** ran for the bus. _____

14. **I** was too frightened to move. _____

15. **We** all like to win games. _____

15
14
13
12
11
10
9
8
7
6
5
4
3
2
1

Push

A **conjunction** is a **joining word**.
It may be used to join **two sentences**.

Colour in your score on the testometer!

I picked up the comic. I read it.   I picked up the comic and read it.

Choose the best conjunction to complete each sentence.

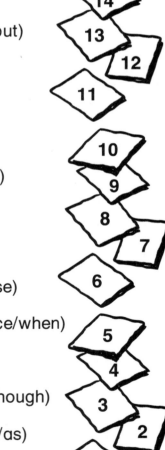

1. I had a bath _____ went to bed. (and/but)

2. An elephant is huge _____ an ant is small. (and/but)

3. I made a sandwich _____ ate it. (and/but)

4. Your towel is wet _____ mine is dry. (and/but)

5. A rabbit is fast _____ a snail is slow. (and/but)

6. I like swimming _____ playing rounders. (and/but)

7. You will get into trouble _____ you talk. (if/so)

8. I was wet _____ it was raining. (if/because)

9. It was hot _____ I took off my jumper. (so/because)

10. The door has been broken _____ I slammed it. (since/when)

11. I ran fast _____ I was late. (if/because)

12. We went for a walk _____ it was very hot. (so/although)

13. I will buy a lolly _____ you give me the money. (if/as)

14. You will get wet _____ you go in the rain. (if/so)

15. My uncle didn't come _____ I didn't see him. (so/if)

We can make new words by **changing** some letters.

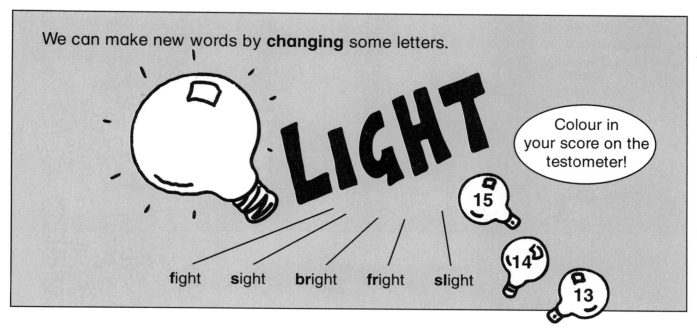

fight   sight   **br**ight   **fr**ight   **sl**ight

Colour in your score on the testometer!

Make some new words.

1. Change the **f** in **f**arm to **ch**. _____

2. Change the **d** in **d**ead to **thr**. _____

3. Change the **w** in **w**ay to **del**. _____

4. Change the **f** in **f**eed to **gr**. _____

5. Change the **n** in **n**erve to **sw**. _____

6. Change the **n** in **n**ew to **scr**. _____

7. Change the **d** in **d**irt to **squ**. _____

8. Change the **m** in **m**oan to **gr**. _____

9. Change the **v** in **v**oice to **ch**. _____

10. Change the **w** in **w**ood to **bl**. _____

11. Change the **l** in **l**oud to **pr**. _____

12. Change the **m** in **m**ow to **borr**. _____

13. Change the **c** in **c**urb to **dist**. _____

14. Change the **d** in **d**are to **bew**. _____

15. Change the **n** in **n**ear to **app**. _____

Possessive pronouns tell us who the **owner** of something is.

These are **my** toys. They are not **yours**. They are mine.

Colour in your score on the testometer!

Some common possessive pronouns are:
my   mine   your   yours   his   her   hers   its
our   ours   their   theirs

Underline the possessive pronoun in each sentence.

1. This is my book.

2. The children picked up their bags.

3. The boy was sure the pen was his.

4. The girl lost her ruler.

5. The robot opened its mouth.

6. "You can't have the ball. It's ours!" Ben shouted.

7. The lady lost her way.

8. This book is mine.

9. We parked our car and got out.

10. I asked the girl if the pen was hers.

11. The ball had their name on it.

12. The children knew the toys were theirs.

13. "I like your picture best," the teacher said to Mary.

14. "Ali broke our model," Amy and Emma complained.

15. This bag belongs to you. It is yours.

Sometimes we **shorten** words and leave letters out. These words are called **contractions**. We use an **apostrophe** to show where letters are missing.

I've got an ice-cream.

Colour in your score on the testometer!

I've = I have

Put in the missing apostrophes in the correct places in these contractions.

1. Im

2. hes

3. Ive

4. wed

5. Ill

6. wouldnt

7. were

8. heres

9. doesnt

10. its

11. wasnt

12. whos

13. wont

14. dont

15. youre

When we write down what people say we use **speech marks**.
The **words the person says** go **inside** the speech marks.

Do you like my pet spider?

Colour in your score on the testometer!

Emma said, "Do you like my pet spider?"

Put in the missing speech marks in these sentences.

1. Hello, Ben said.

2. It's nice to see you, Sam replied.

3. What a lovely day! exclaimed Ben.

4. Yes it's so warm, Sam answered.

5. The weather forecast said it would rain, Ben said.

6. I don't think it will, Sam replied.

7. I can see a few black clouds, Ben commented.

8. I think they will pass over, Sam said.

9. Where are you off to? Ben asked.

10. I'm going to town to do some shopping, Sam answered.

11. May I come? Ben asked.

12. Yes, of course. Shall we walk or wait for a bus? Sam said.

13. Let's walk, Ben suggested.

14. I think I can feel a few spots of rain, Sam said.

15. Let's get the bus, then, said Ben.

A **proper noun** is a **special** (or **particular**) name of a **person**, **place** or **thing**. Proper nouns always begin with a **capital letter**.

Colour in your score on the testometer!

AMERICA

New York

Here is **W**ayne.   **N**ew **Y**ork is in **A**merica.   This is the **E**mpire **S**tate **B**uilding.

Rewrite these proper nouns correctly.

1. anna _____

2. mr khan _____

3. doctor parker _____

4. bert _____

5. washington _____

6. green park _____

7. high street _____

8. charing cross station _____

9. daily mirror _____

10. tottenham hotspur _____

11. wednesday _____

12. february _____

13. christmas _____

14. golden sands hotel _____

15. moscow _____

Answers

Test 1

The missing prefix is in **bold**.

1. **un**pack
2. **un**well
3. **dis**place
4. **dis**trust
5. **un**fair
6. **un**happy
7. **dis**agree
8. **dis**may
9. **un**load
10. **un**bolt
11. **dis**honest
12. **un**do
13. **dis**arm
14. **dis**charge
15. **un**cover

Test 2

1. disappeared
2. spoke
3. chased
4. brushed
5. painted
6. knocking
7. drinking
8. groaned
9. pushing
10. shining
11. roared
12. crashed
13. flapped
14. hopped
15. came

Test 3

The correct phoneme is in **bold**.

1. m**oo**n
2. tr**ea**t
3. gr**ow**
4. gl**ue**
5. r**oa**d
6. cl**aw**
7. p**ai**nt
8. b**ur**n
9. **ow**l
10. th**ir**sty
11. yesterd**ay**
12. narr**ow**
13. r**ou**nd
14. s**au**cer
15. b**oi**l

Test 4

1. thimble
2. feeble
3. grumble
4. jungle
5. angle
6. single
7. handle
8. needle
9. ladle
10. purple
11. simple
12. steeple
13. uncle
14. circle
15. article

Test 5

1. Where do you come from?
2. What a funny name!
3. The spaceship landed.
4. A door opened slowly.
5. Run for your life!
6. Who is there?
7. What do you want?
8. It's not fair!
9. This is terrible!
10. The sun set in the sky.
11. The bees buzzed near the flowers.
12. How did the car crash?
13. When did the letter come?
14. Stop that at once!
15. We have sausages and chips for tea.

Test 6

1. Little Bo Peep said, "I've lost my sheep."
2. The mouse said, "I ran up the clock."
3. Humpty Dumpty said, "I fell off the wall."
4. Incy Wincy Spider said, "I climbed up the water spout."
5. Little Jack Horner said, "I sat in the corner."
6. "I marched up the hill," said the grand old Duke of York.
7. "I went to London," said Dick Whittington.
8. "I met a wolf," said Little Red Riding Hood.
9. "I climbed a beanstalk," said Jack.
10. "I ran away," said the gingerbread man.
11. Hansel said, "I got lost in a wood."
12. "I went to the ball," Cinderella said.
13. Old King Cole said, "I'm a merry old soul."
14. "I made some tarts," said the Queen of Hearts.
15. "I'm very ugly," the troll said.

Test 7

1. bat cat dog
2. elephant fox goat
3. hen jaguar kangaroo
4. lion monkey ostrich
5. penguin rat seal
6. panda swan zebra
7. beetle donkey hamster mouse
8. donkey giraffe ox worm
9. cat cow crab
10. bear bird bull
11. parrot pelican pike
12. sardine shark snake
13. tiger toad trout turtle
14. gerbil giraffe gnu goat
15. badger bee bird buffalo

Test 8

1. walked
2. hopped
3. carried
4. moved
5. arrived
6. begged
7. copied
8. held
9. brought
10. saw
11. spoke
12. took
13. taught
14. wrote
15. came

Test 9

1. My friends are Sam, Emma, Abdi and Shanaz.
2. March, June, May and July are months of the year.
3. I like red, blue, yellow and green.
4. The four seasons are spring, summer, autumn and winter.
5. I have a dog, a cat, a fish and a budgie.
6. I hate sprouts, cabbage, parsnips and leeks.
7. I would like a bike, a pen, a book and a bag for Christmas.
8. Art, science, music and maths are good subjects.
9. In my bag I have a pen, a ruler, a rubber and a book.
10. London, Rome, Paris and Vienna are all capital cities.
11. I have been to France, Spain, Greece and Malta.
12. On the farm I saw some cows, sheep, pigs and hens.
13. On the rock there was a beetle, an ant, a slug and a snail.
14. Crisps, chips, chocolate and biscuits are not healthy.
15. In the sky you can see clouds, the sun, the moon and stars.

Test 10

1. fat (or) her (or) the
2. the (or) moth
3. ear (or) hear
4. one
5. now (or) no
6. use (or) be (or) cause (or) us
7. den
8. end
9. man (or) any (or) an
10. eel (or) heel
11. tag (or) age (or) stag
12. quest (or) on
13. row (or) arrow
14. me
15. my

Test 11

1. carpenter
2. tailor
3. farmer
4. jockey
5. optician
6. airport
7. garage
8. dock
9. library
10. palace
11. sink
12. cot
13. kettle
14. spoon
15. wardrobe

Test 12

1. chairs
2. foxes
3. coaches
4. bushes
5. glasses
6. berries
7. children
8. men
9. bike
10. box
11. bunch
12. dish
13. copy
14. lorry
15. sheep

Test 13

1. **w**rite
2. **k**nee
3. **k**now
4. **w**reck
5. **w**rist
6. **w**restle
7. **k**nock
8. **k**night
9. num**b**
10. **g**nat
11. clim**b**
12. crum**b**
13. thum**b**
14. **g**nome
15. **g**naw

Test 14

1. heavy
2. straight
3. tall
4. funny
5. loud
6. muddy
7. dirty
8. fizzy
9. open
10. busy
11. empty
12. old
13. beautiful
14. sharp
15. handsome

Test 15

1. colourful
2. painful
3. careful
4. thankful
5. helpful
6. useless
7. hopeless
8. thoughtless
9. lawless
10. helpless
11. wonder
12. heart
13. grace
14. faith
15. pity